The Ramayan

Text: Sadhu Amrutvijaydas

Paintings: Vasudeo Kamath

SWAMINARAYAN AKSHARPITH

1st Edition: April 2004

ISBN: 81-7526-249-4

Copies: 3,000
Rs: 100-00

Printed & Published by:
Swaminarayan Aksharpith
Shahibaug Road,
Amdavad-4
Gujarat, India.

Websites:
www.swaminarayan.org
kids.swaminarayan.org
www.mandir.org
www.akshardham.com

Preface

The Ramayan is one of the most popular and widely studied epics of Hinduism.

Many versions of the Ramayan have become popular throughout the world. The stories presented in this publication are based on the original Valmiki, Tulsi, Girdharkrut texts and other popular translations.

Bhagwan Swaminarayan and the spiritual lineage of God-realised Sadhus in the Swaminarayan Sampraday have also enthusiastically promoted the inspiring ideals of the Ramayan.

This publication, inspired by His Divine Holiness Pramukh Swami Maharaj, is a very brief account of the Ramayan, incorporating its major stories and highlighting its salient messages. At the end, a selection of Bhagwan Swaminarayan's references to the Ramayan in the Vachanamrut - a collection of Bhagwan Swaminarayan's spiritual discourses - has also been included, to illustrate how the Ramayan's messages can be applied in practical spiritual life.

We hope that children and teenagers everywhere will be inspired by the teachings of the Ramayan and will be motivated to study it in greater depth.

We thank Vasudeo Kamath for the 26 excellent watercolour paintings, Sadhu Amrutvijaydas for the script and Sadhu Shrijiswarupdas for the book design and layout.

- **Swaminarayan Aksharpith**

CONTENTS

Introduction

The Ramayan is the oldest poem in the world. It was composed in the ancient Indian language of Sanskrit by the great Sage Valmiki.

This epic poem consists of 24,000 *shloks* or verses divided into 500 chapters, which are arranged into seven Kands (sections): Bal, Ayodhya, Aranya, Kishkindha, Sundar, Yuddh and Uttar.

The Ramayan is the true story of Bhagwan Shri Ram, son of King Dashrath of Ayodhya. Although his actions are like those of an ordinary man, Ram was an incarnation of Lord Vishnu. From birth, Ram was endowed with godly virtues. He lived by the injunctions of the scriptures, sacrificing his personal happiness for the good of his subjects, and so was known as Maryada Purushottam. Ram lived for 14 years in the forest to fulfil his father's promise and uphold his honour. During this time his wife, Sita, was kidnapped by the demon Ravan. Ram, with the help of Hanuman, Sugriv, Jambuvan and other monkeys and bears, defeated Ravan and rescued Sita. This grand story of the victory of good over evil is a thrilling and moving story which describes the different shades of human emotions and instincts.

The Ramayan depicts the character and virtues of an ideal husband, wife, parent, child, brother, sister and a friend. Its message of morality inspires both young and old to develop a lofty and sublime character that will bring peace to them, their families, to society and to the world.

The universal appeal of the Ramayan is illustrated by its widespread acceptance in many countries, where its teachings are studied and practiced. Its timeless messages have inspired many great works of art, dance, drama, music and literature throughout the ages.

A small publication like this can only serve to whet one's appetite for a more detailed study of this truly remarkable and enlightening epic poem.

Sage Valmiki Writes the Ramayan

The noble Sage Valmiki lived in his ashram on the banks of the beautiful river Tamasa in North India.

One day, while he was deep in thought, Naradji arrived. Pleasantly surprised, Valmiki asked Naradji the question which he had been pondering over for sometime, "Is there a perfect man in this world who is wise and virtuous in all respects?"

Naradji revealed, "Yes. There is the noble king of the Ikshvaku dynasty – Ram. He is perfect in every way." Naradji then continued to narrate the entire story of Shri Ram to Valmiki.

After Naradji's departure, Valmiki meditated on the glorious personality of Ram and then went to the banks of the river Tamasa for a bath.

As he admired the natural beauty of the riverside, he saw two *kraunch* birds perched on a tree in full bloom. Very much in love, they were happily chirping away in their sweet and melodious voice, totally unaware of what was happening around them. Suddenly, the male *kraunch* bird was pierced by the arrow of a cruel hunter. The female's joy turned to distress and her mournful wail filled Valmiki's heart with sadness. He cursed the sinful hunter, "Since you have killed this bird while it was making love, you shall never find peace." To Valmiki's surprise, the words of his curse were naturally spoken in the rhythmic metre of a *shlok*. Then, completing his rituals, he returned to his ashram.

After a while, Lord Brahma appeared. Valmiki honoured him and then Brahma revealed, "I inspired the *shlok* you spoke on the riverbank and wish you to compose the story of Ram, as told to you by Naradji, in the form of a great poem in the same metre."

Valmiki accepted the task. He sat amid the serene and sublime atmosphere of his ashram and began to recall the story of Ram and his victory over Ravan to rescue Sita. Hence, by divine inspiration he composed the Ramayan.

Later, he taught the entire poem to the twin sons of Ram – Lav and Kush. They, in turn, travelled from ashram to ashram, reciting this epic poem in their sweet voices.

The Birth of Ram

From his majestic palace in the capital city of Ayodhya, King Dashrath ruled over the kingdom of Koshal. He was a wise and just king who was loved and admired by all his subjects.

Despite his enormous wealth and widespread popularity, he was sad because he had no son to continue his lineage.

So, with the blessings of his guru, Sage Vasishtha, the king requested Sage Rishyashringa to perform the Ashwamedh Yagna.

All the necessary preparations were made and at the selected auspicious moment, the *yagna* was commenced. Then, at the appropriate time, Rishyashringa recited verses from the Atharva Veda, initiating the Putrakam Yagna. Dashrath and his wives devoutly performed the *yagna* rituals, as guided by the sage.

Towards the end, a splendid, divine figure adorned with rich ornaments rose from the midst of the *yagna* flames. He held a golden pot of *payasam*, which he presented to King Dashrath and instructed him, "Give this *payasam* to your wives. By drinking it, they will bear you virtuous sons."

The king was overjoyed. He accepted the pot and called his wives Kaushalya, Sumitra and Kaikeyi. He gave about half of the *payasam* to Kaushalya; of the remainder he gave about half each to Sumitra and Kaikeyi; then the remaining small amount of *payasam* he again gave to Sumitra.

The *yagna* was thus successfully concluded.

In due course, Dashrath's queens bore four sons: Ram was born to Kaushalya, Bharat to Kaikeyi and the twins, Lakshman and Shatrughna to Sumitra. As the news spread there was rejoicing throughout the kingdom. The births of the princes were celebrated on a grand scale.

The four brothers grew to have tremendous love for each other. They were taught all the skills necessary for princes and excelled in every way. They were strong, handsome, virtuous and captured the hearts of the people.

The Story of Sita

King Janak was the wise and noble ruler of the kingdom of Videha and a close friend of King Dashrath.

Once, due to a prolonged drought, a terrible famine befell the kingdom of Videha. King Janak was concerned about the welfare of his subjects and consulted the learned Brahmins of his kingdom for ways to help them. In addition to certain immediate measures, they advised him to perform a *yagna* and pray for rain. A suitable site was selected in the capital city of Mithila and King Janak himself began ploughing the field to clean, level and prepare it for the *yagna*.

One day, as he pulled the plough, its tip struck a case and cracked it open. To his surprise, he saw a beautiful baby girl lying within. He picked up the child and rushed to his queen, Sunayana, to describe how he had unearthed the heavenly child.

As they were childless, they accepted the infant girl as a gift from Mother Earth. Since she had been tuned up by the tip of a plough, they named her Sita. She also became known as Janki, the daughter of Janak. Believing her to be an incarnation of goddess Lakshmi, King Janak and Queen Sunayana raised Sita with tremendous love and care.

Sita Plays with Lord Shiv's Bow

As the years passed, Sita grew up into a charming, virtuous girl of remarkable ability.

In a special room of the palace, King Janak kept a giant bow which had been presented to one of his ancestors, Devraat, by Lord Shiv. It was very heavy and required many strong men merely to lift it.

The bow had been preserved in the family with great reverence and was worshipped with flowers and incense daily. Every day, Queen Sunayana personally swept the prayer room in which it was housed. But, since the bow was too heavy for her to lift, she was unable to clean the area surrounding it. Then, one day, as she was busy with some other work she instructed Sita to sweep the room instead.

As she swept the room, Sita noticed the dust around the bow. So, she casually lifted the giant bow, placed it on the opposite side and completed her work. Then she began playing with the bow as if it were a mere toy. When Sunayana saw that the bow had been moved, she asked Sita about it. Sita told her that since there was dust surrounding the bow, she had lifted it and placed it on the other side of the room so that she could clean the area. Sunayana narrated Sita's incredible feat to King Janak. He, too, was astonished.

So, King Janak resolved that he would give Sita in marriage only to him who could lift and string this giant, heavy bow of Lord Shiv.

Lured by Sita's beauty many powerful princes tried to string the mighty bow of Lord Shiv, but failed. King Janak awaited the day when a worthy and virtuous prince would fulfil his condition.

Ram Slays the Demoness Tataka

The courage and expertise in the art of warfare of Ram and his brothers became well-known to all.

Once, Sage Vishwamitra came to King Dashrath and requested, "I want you to allow Ram, your eldest son, to come with me to kill the demons, Subahu and Marich, who are disturbing my *yagna*. I will teach him all the necessary skills and no harm will come to him."

Dashrath was at first reluctant because of his attachment to Ram, but then he agreed to send both Ram and Lakshman with Vishwamitra to help him.

Soon the three left and arrived at the banks of the river Saryu. Here, Vishwamitra taught Ram the powerful mantras Bala and Atibala. "With these, hunger, thirst and fatigue will not affect you," Vishwamitra explained. Then they proceeded and entered the Tataka Van – a dark and frightening forest inhabited by the demoness, Tataka. She killed all who entered without her permission. She was previously the beautiful wife of a Yaksha named Sund. They had a son called Marich. Once, she and her son assaulted Sage Agastya, who cursed them to become demons. Thus, they began their life of harassing the innocent. Tataka had the strength of a thousand elephants.

Vishwamitra instructed Ram, "As a Kshatriya, it is your duty to slay her to protect the innocent."

With these instructions, Ram stringed his bow in readiness. Tataka soon appeared and attacked Ram with huge rocks. So Ram took aim, shot his arrows and killed the evil demoness.

Victorious, the princes and Vishwamitra proceeded towards his ashram. There, Vishwamitra began to perform the *yagna* while Ram and Lakshman stood on guard. On the last day of the *yagna*, Marich and Subahu raided the ashram with the intention of sabotaging the *yagna*. But Ram and Lakshman were too skillful for the demons. Subahu was killed, while the arrow that hit Marich hurled him hundreds of kilometres away, but did not kill him.

Thus, Ram and Lakshman enabled Vishwamitra to complete his *yagna*.

Then they all left the ashram to return to Ayodhya.

Ram Wins the Hand of Sita

On the way, Vishwamitra led the heroic princes to King Janak's palace in Mithila to see the great bow of Lord Shiv.

King Janak was deeply spiritual and well versed in the scriptures. He welcomed the trio and honoured them appropriately. Vishwamitra introduced the two princes to Janak, who expressed his joy and felt truly blessed by their presence. Then Vishwamitra requested Janak, "Ram and Lakshman would like to see the majestic bow of Lord Shiv which has been worshipped by your family for many generations."

Immediately, Janak ordered his ministers to make arrangements for the princes to see the wonderful bow. As they waited, King Janak related the story of the famous bow, "Once Daksh, father-in-law of Shiv, was performing a *yagna* in the presence of the *devas*. Daksh had not invited Shiv and refused to give him his rightful share of the offerings in the *yagna*. Angered by this insult, Shiv stormed into the *yagna* arena and threatened the *devas*, 'You will all pay dearly for permitting this injustice to me. With this powerful bow, I will cut off your heads!' Struck with fear, the *devas* rushed to appease Shiv. They humbly fell at his feet and begged for forgiveness. As quickly as he was angered, Shiv was pacified. Pleased by the respect he was given, he withdrew his threat, to the great relief of the *devas*. Shiv showed his pleasure by gifting his mighty bow to the *devas*. They, in turn, entrusted it to the care of Devraat, my ancestor. Since then, this giant bow has been worshipped in my family." Janak also revealed that he had decided to marry his daughter, Sita, to a worthy prince who could string the bow. As yet, nobody had succeeded.

Just then, the magnificent bow was wheeled in. Vishwamitra instructed Ram to view the famous bow. Ram looked intently at it and then requested permission from the sage and the king to string the bow. It was granted. Everyone watched in excited anticipation as Ram confidently picked up the bow with his left hand and strung it. As he did so, the thunderous snap of the bow breaking in two was heard all around. Cheers of joy echoed everywhere. Janak, too, smiled in jubilation; for Ram had fulfilled his condition to be Sita's husband. Sita was also happy that Ram had successfully strung the bow and placed a garland of flowers around his neck. With Vishwamitra's approval, the offer of marriage was accepted and messengers were sent to Ayodhya to invite King Dashrath for the grand wedding.

Encounter with Parshuram

Dashrath received Janak's messengers with respect and listened attentively as they described the momentous events that had occurred. He and his queens were overjoyed to learn that Ram had won the hand of Sita in marriage.

The next morning, Dashrath, with his sons, queens, sages, ministers and others, left for Mithila. The journey took four days. On their arrival, Janak rushed to personally receive the venerable king and his entourage. Suitable arrangements had been made for the stay of the royal party.

In the presence of the sages, the auspicious day for the wedding was fixed and preparations for the royal occasion proceeded at full speed.

Meanwhile, Janak had an idea and requested Dashrath to come to his court with his sons. Then, Janak offered his other daughter, Urmila, in marriage to Lakshman. The match was greeted with total approval.

Then, Vishwamitra proposed that Mandvi and Shrutakirti, the beautiful daughters of Kushadhvaj, Janak's brother, be married to Bharat and Shatrughna. This, too, was accepted. Thus, on the specified day, amid great celebrations, the marriages of the four princes and princesses took place.

After the wedding, Vishwamitra took leave to return to his ashram and King Dashrath led the newlyweds back towards Ayodhya. On the way, Parshuram – the destroyer of Kshatriyas – suddenly appeared and arrogantly challenged Ram, "You have strung the bow of Lord Shiv. Vishwakarma, the architect of the gods, had made two such bows. The other, which he gave to Vishnu, is with me. If you can string this bow then it will be proof of your skill and strength, and you will be eligible to fight with me."

Ram calmly and respectfully replied, "I accept your challenge." Then, he took the bow from Parshuram and effortlessly stringed it with an arrow. He told Parshuram, "My arrows never return without hitting their target. So, as I do not want to kill you, shall I destroy the fruits of your austerities or your power of motion which allows you to travel wherever you wish?"

Parshuram realised he had been defeated and submitted the fruits of his austerities.

After the encounter, King Dashrath, Ram, Sita and others safely reached Ayodhya to a warm and joyous reception.

Ram Sent into Exile

For the next 12 years, Ram and Sita lived happily in Ayodhya. Ram's wise and just ways made him the people's favourite.

One day, King Dashrath decided it was time to enthrone the young prince Ram as the king of Koshal. He sought the advice of Vasishtha and other seniors, who agreed that it was a wonderful idea. Ram was summoned and accordingly informed. Dashrath said, "We will perform the coronation ceremony tomorrow." All the citizens greeted the king's decision with unanimous approval and everyone began to prepare for the celebrations.

Meanwhile, the news reached Manthara, the hunch-back maid of Bharat's mother, Kaikeyi. She poisoned Kaikeyi's mind, "Bharat is away at present and if you allow Ram to be king, your rights and privileges will be lost. Act before it is too late." Thus, she convinced Kaikeyi to use the two boons that Dashrath had promised her for her service to him during the war between the gods and demons.

As suggested, Kaikeyi approached King Dashrath and requested him to grant her the two boons he had promised. She demanded, "Install Bharat as the king and send Ram into exile for 14 years." Dashrath was shattered on hearing these senseless demands. He tried to persuade her to ask for something else, but Kaikeyi was stubborn and unwilling to change her demands.

Heartbroken, Dashrath had no choice but to do as Kaikeyi demanded. Ram was informed of the changed situation by Kaikeyi herself. Despite the sudden change in circumstances, the joy on his face was the same as when he had entered to see his father. Being an ideal son, he happily accepted the demands and vowed to uphold his father's honour by obeying them.

As the news spread, everyone was shocked. Now, instead of being crowned king, Ram, together with Sita and Lakshman, prepared to leave Ayodhya, wearing only clothes made from tree bark; sacrificing their luxurious palace life, for a simple life in the forests. The people, still struggling to believe that Ram had been banished, lined the streets to give them an emotional farewell, as they were driven in a chariot by Sumantra.

Thus, Ram, Sita and Lakshman began their life in the forest. First, they stayed with Guha, a hunter-chief. Here, Ram instructed Sumantra to return to Ayodhya. After his departure, they arrived at the ashram of Sage Bharadvaj. From here they went to Chitrakut hill, where they built an ashram on the banks of the river Malayavati.

The Golden Sandals

Meanwhile, back in Ayodhya, King Dashrath, unable to bear the grief of separation from his beloved Ram, passed away. This tragic news was conveyed to Bharat and Shatrughna who were in Rajagriha, the capital city of Kekaya, visiting King Ashvapati, the father of Kaikeyi. The two princes rushed back to Ayodhya, where they were informed of the tragic events. Kaikeyi, beaming with joy and satisfaction, explained to Bharat how she had secured King Dashrath's promise to banish Ram and crown him as king. Bharat listened, shocked and speechless. Angered by the actions of his mother, he told her that her wicked behaviour was totally inappropriate. She tried to convince him that she had done all this for him, but Bharat was not interested. He resolved to bring Ram back from the forests and then left to perform the final rites of his father.

After the period of mourning was over, the royal sages and ministers requested Bharat to accept the vacant throne. But he refused, saying, "I am not the king. The kingdom and I belong to Ram. He is the rightful heir. I will go to the forest, crown him as king, and return with him." Sage Vasishtha was pleased at Bharat's understanding, integrity and observance of *dharma*.

Thereafter, Bharat and Shatrughna, together with Vasishtha, their mothers, ministers and a large army left to meet Ram. When they arrived at Ram's ashram at Chitrakut, Bharat and Shatrughna hurried to meet Ram and fell at his feet. It was an emotional reunion. The news of King Dashrath's death was conveyed to Ram and Lakshman; they were deeply grieved.

Then, Bharat pleaded with Ram to accept the throne and return to Ayodhya. But Ram firmly refused. The seniors of the royal court also tried to convince him, but Ram was adamant. Eventually, the sages agreed with Ram that it was his duty to uphold his father's promise. Ram told Bharat, "You must rule the kingdom." Reluctantly, Bharat agreed to rule the kingdom as Ram's representative, but refused to sit on the throne. From the articles he had brought for Ram's coronation, Bharat took out a pair of golden sandals. He requested Ram to wear them. After sanctifying them, Ram gave the sandals back to Bharat. The latter touched them to his head in reverence and revealed that he would place them on the throne to represent Ram until he returned from exile. Bharat also vowed to eat, dress and live simply. Then, Ram embraced Bharat before they parted.

On returning to Ayodhya, Bharat placed the sandals on the throne to symbolize that Ram was king. He then governed the kingdom from the nearby town of Nandigram.

Lakshman Disfigures Surpankha

Soon after everyone had left, Ram decided that they should leave Chitrakut. They descended the hill and arrived at the ashram of Sage Atri. There, his wife, Ansuya, praised Sita for her faithfulness to Ram and presented her some gifts. The next morning, the royal trio left the ashram. They passed through the Dandaka forest and soon arrived at Panchvati, where they built an ashram. They lived simply, yet happily and peacefully, for many years, with Lakshman dutifully serving Ram and Sita.

One day, Ram, Lakshman and Sita were relaxing at their hermitage in Panchvati. Suddenly, a demoness appeared. Seeing the handsome Ram, she fell in love with him and demanded, "I am Surpankha, sister of Ravan, the king of Lanka. I insist that you marry me." Ram was amused. He told her, "I am a married man and can't oblige you. However, Lakshman, my younger brother, is handsome and brave. Why don't you ask him." She did. But Lakshman replied, "I am a servant of Ram and it is not proper for you to be the wife of a servant." These refusals enraged Surpankha, who threatened Ram, "It is this woman, your wife, who stands between us. I will kill her and make you my husband."

Surpankha's repeated threats and advances angered Ram. He instructed Lakshman, "Punish this demoness and send her away." Lakshman promptly cut off Surpankha's nose and ears. With blood streaming from her face, she ran away screaming to her brothers Khara and Dushana. Khara vowed revenge and returned with Dushana and fourteen thousand demons to kill Ram. Alert to the danger, Ram and Lakshman strung their bows and destroyed the enemy, killing Khara, Dushana and most of the others. However, one of the demons, Akampa, escaped and rushed to Lanka to inform Ravan of what had happened. Ravan was angered by the loss of his brothers and soldiers.

Surpankha also went to Ravan to complain about Ram. She added, "Sita is Ram's beautiful wife, and would be an ideal wife for you." Tempted by this, Ravan thought of a plan to kidnap Sita and punish Ram.

The Golden Deer

Ravan approached Marich and told him his plan.

Hearing it, Marich warned Ravan that Ram was no ordinary man; that he was a man of divine virtues and strength; that confronting him like this was not a wise thing to do. Thus, Marich tried to change Ravan's mind, but he did not listen.

In fact, Ravan threatened to kill Marich if he did not obey. So, after much thought, Marich decided that it would be better to die at the hands of the noble Ram rather than the evil Ravan.

The plan was put into action. Marich appeared before Ram's hermitage in the form of a golden deer. Attracted to its beautiful form, Sita requested Ram to capture it for her. At first he tried to dissuade her, but due to her insistence he agreed. However, before Ram left, he told Lakshman to protect Sita.

Marich drew Ram a long distance away from his hermitage by using his magical powers. Then, when Ram had the deer in sight he struck it with an arrow. Wounded, Marich appeared in his original form and let out a cry imitating Ram's voice, "Save me! O Sita! O Lakshman!"

Back at the hermitage, Sita and Lakshman heard the cry for help. Lakshman knew it was a trick, but Sita insisted that he go to help Ram. Lakshman attempted to explain to Sita that nothing would happen to Ram. But Sita was not convinced. So, out of her fear for Ram, she uttered bitter words to him, "You know Ram is in danger yet you are not concerned. You are not a true brother of Ram, but his enemy. Your intentions are evil. Is this what you have waited for all these years? You wish to see Ram die so that you can take me. But, I will give up my life rather than surrender to any other man except Ram." Sita's outburst stunned Lakshman. Against his wish, Lakshman agreed to go to Ram's aid. But, before leaving, he drew a circle on the ground around their hermitage with his bow and instructed Sita, "Remain within this circle and no harm will come to you." Then, reluctantly, Lakshman left to help Ram.

Ravan Kidnaps Sita

With Sita alone, Ravan approached the hermitage in the garb of an aged sannyasi and begged for alms. Ravan befriended Sita and his comforting words made her feel compelled to help him. She offered him fruits and vegetables but Ravan deceitfully laid down a condition. He said, "O beautiful maiden! I am a sannyasi and I do not accept alms which are given from within the boundary of a home." Hearing this, and without thinking of the possible danger, Sita stepped out of the protective circle – the Lakshman Rekha – drawn by Lakshman to hand over the alms.

Bewitched by the beauty of Sita, Ravan then talked to her at length on various topics of worldly interest. He also expressed affection for her, as a result of which Sita questioned his motives. Then Ravan revealed, "I am Ravan, the demon king of Lanka. Seeing your heavenly beauty, I intensely desire to have you as my wife. Ram does not deserve you."

Sita protested at Ravan's insulting words, but then suddenly, Ravan grabbed her. Sita tried to break his grip, but she was not successful. She was outside the area of protection that Lakshman had marked out. Ravan pulled Sita onto his flying chariot and headed towards Lanka, with Sita protesting and seething with anger. She appealed to the trees, animals and birds in the forest, but nobody was able to help her.

Jatayu Fights with Ravan

Eventually, Sita's desperate cries for help from the chariot were heard by the aged Jatayu – king of the eagles and a good friend of King Dashrath. Jatayu was sleeping on a tree top; he awoke, confronted Ravan and tried to reason with him, but Ravan paid no attention. So Jatayu challenged him and warned that he would not let him take Sita.

Ravan was furious by this unplanned interference and immediately attacked Jatayu with arrows and other weapons. Sita tried to obstruct his efforts. A furious battle took place. The jungle became filled with the sound of chaos. Jatayu was injured but he fought valiantly with his claws, beak and wings. He wounded Ravan, broke his bow and grounded his chariot. But Ravan still had Sita firmly in his grip. The intense fighting took its toll on the aged Jatayu. He was tired and his attacks on Ravan now had little effect. Seizing this opportunity, Ravan took his sword and cut off Jatayu's wings. And then forcing Sita back into his chariot, he flew off again into the sky, leaving behind the mortally wounded Jatayu.

Ignoring Sita's protests, Ravan sped towards Lanka. Sita called out to Ram and Lakshman for help, but it was of no use.

As they passed a mountain, Sita spotted some monkeys. She quickly removed some of her ornaments and tore a piece from her upper garment. She tied the jewels in the torn piece of cloth and threw the bundle out of the chariot, still shouting out for Ram and Lakshman to save her.

Soon, however, Ravan's chariot reached Lanka, where Ravan tried to persuade Sita to marry him. She firmly refused and so Ravan had her sent to Ashok Vatika, a beautiful garden where she would be kept under watch and he could continue to try persuading her to be his wife.

Ram Meets Jatayu

When Ram and Lakshman returned to the hermitage, a strange silence greeted them. They realised that Sita was not there. They searched nearby, but could not find her. So, they ventured further into the forest, but still she was no where to be seen.

Despondent, as they were walking through the forest they saw the injured Jatayu. They ran over to the dying eagle king and served him some water. As Ram gently and lovingly caressed him, Jatayu told them, "Ravan has carried away Sita to Lanka. I tried to prevent him but because of old age I did not have the energy to fight him fiercely."

Having managed to provide Ram with the necessary information, Jatayu passed away. Ram and Lakshman were grieved to lose such a caring father figure. They took Jatayu's body to the banks of the river Godavari and performed his funeral rites.

They then proceeded south, guided by the information given by Jatayu.

Suddenly, Kabandh, a headless demon, with long arms, a mouth in his stomach and one eye above it, seized them. Ram and Lakshman cut of his arms and maimed the demon. Kabandh asked them who they were. When he learnt that the person in front of him was Ram in search of the kidnapped Sita, Kabandh narrated his story, "My name was Dhanu. I was cursed to live in the forest as a demon. I have lost my powers, but if you cremate me they will be restored and I can guide you in your search."

Ram and Lakshman cremated Kabandh and from the pyre, Dhanu, a handsome, heavenly figure emerged. He told Ram, "Go to the Rishyamuk mountain, near Lake Pampa. There, you will find Sugriv, whose brother, Vali, has driven him out of the kingdom. Sugriv will be able to help you."

Then Dhanu respectfully took leave of Ram and Lakshman.

Ram Accepts Shabri's Devotion

Filled with hope by Kabandh's guidance, Ram and Lakshman headed towards Lake Pampa. On its west bank was the ashram of the devout Shabri. She was an old woman who had devoutly served Matang Rishi for many years. She had been offering devotion and austerities and awaiting the *darshan* of Ram.

The two princes entered the ashram. Shabri was overjoyed. She bowed respectfully at Ram's feet and expressed the contentment she felt by his *darshan,* "This is the reward for my austerities and service to the rishis. By your *darshan* I will certainly attain salvation." With heartfelt devotion she offered them berries that she had collected. Both Ram and Lakshman ate the berries and were pleased by her sincere service and devotion. Shabri stood humbly before Ram and said, "My wish has been fulfilled by your *darshan.* Now I am ready to enter heaven." Ram blessed her and praising her faithful service and devotion, he said, "One who has many worldly accomplishments and abilities, but does not possess true devotion, is worthless like a cloud without water. You possess unflinching devotion and so you will attain my abode." Bowing again at Ram's feet, Shabri narrated the words of her guru, Matang Rishi, who, before his demise many years before, had predicted that Ram would visit her and reward her devotion. Then, with Ram's permission, she prepared a fire and entered it. By the merits of her lifelong devotion she assumed a divine form and entered heaven.

From here Ram and Lakshman proceeded to Rishyamuk Mountain, refreshed and strengthened by their meeting with Shabri.

Hanuman Finds Sita

As the two princes approached the Rishyamuk mountain, they met Hanuman, Sugriv's minister. He explained to Ram that Vali, Sugriv's powerful elder brother, had taken Sugriv's wife and expelled him from his kingdom.

Ram explained his search for Sita and then Hanuman carried both the princes to Sugriv. A friendship developed between Ram and Sugriv. Ram promised to defeat Vali for him and, in return, Sugriv promised to help Ram find Sita.

Pleased with Ram's offer, Sugriv revealed, "Some time ago, I was on the mountain top when I saw a beautiful woman being carried away in a flying chariot. She was crying 'Ram, Ram' and she dropped a bundle of ornaments." Sugriv showed the ornaments to Ram and Lakshman. One-by-one Ram inspected the ornaments. Ram then asked Lakshman if he recognised them. Lakshman said, "I do not recognise the ear-rings, necklace or bracelets, but the anklets definitely belong to Sita. I know this since I see them when I bow at her feet daily." Ram was lost in thought about the harsh treatment Sita had endured at the hands of Ravan. Lakshman and Sugriv consoled him, assuring that the evil Ravan would soon be defeated.

First, though, Ram asked Sugriv to challenge Vali to a duel. It was during this fight that Ram killed Vali. Before he died, Vali placed his son, Angad, in the care of Ram. Sugriv was then crowned king. After some time, Sugriv sent Hanuman in search of Sita. Hanuman leaped across the ocean and landed in Lanka. He assumed a small form and searched Ravan's palace but was unable to find her. He then went to the garden called Ashok Vatika. There, under a tree he spotted the thin, forlorn figure of Sita. He went up to her, introduced himself as Ram's messenger and gave her the ring bearing Ram's emblem as proof of his genuine identity.

Sita was overcome with emotion. Hanuman reassured her that Ram would soon come to rescue her and defeat the wicked Ravan. Then he left Sita. But, following a battle in which he killed Ravan's son, Aksha, Hanuman allowed himself to be caught by Ravan's soldiers. He was taken to Ravan, where he warned of the dangers that awaited him if he did not release Sita. Ravan ignored the warning and instructed his men to set fire to Hanuman's tail, after wrapping it in oil-soaked rags. Then, when his tail was lit, Hanuman assumed a larger form and jumped around the city setting fire to everything. While everything burnt, Sita remained unharmed in Ashok Vatika. Hanuman returned to report his findings to Ram.

Vibhishan Joins Ram

Meanwhile, angered and worried by the turmoil caused by Hanuman, Ravan called an urgent meeting of his ministers and army generals. He described the strength and capabilities of Ram and his huge army of monkeys. Ravan's ministers and generals sought to pacify him and recalled his famous victories over powerful opponents. This comforted Ravan and his confidence grew.

However, amid all this praise, Vibhishan, the virtuous brother of Ravan, stood up and warned him of the divine skills, righteousness and other noble virtues of Ram. In conclusion, Vibhishan advised Ravan, "Return Sita to Ram, otherwise we will all be killed and this city will be destroyed." But Ravan, blinded by his desire for Sita, ignored him and discounted the threat Ram posed.

Even Kumbhakaran, Ravan's giant brother who slept for six months at a time, scolded him for abducting Sita, but still expressed his readiness to fight for him. Then, Vibhishan again voiced his disapproval and urged Ravan to return Sita. But Ravan was not open to reason and he angrily accused Vibhishan of being a traitor in the guise of a friend. Hurt by these words, Vibhishan realised that Ravan did not want his help and so he left Lanka, with four companions, to join Ram.

When Vibhishan reached the opposite shore, he was surrounded and questioned by some of the monkey warriors. Vibhishan revealed his identity as Ravan's brother and the events leading to his split from him. He appealed, "I have come to take refuge at the feet of Ram. Please take me to him."

This message was conveyed to Ram and a discussion began as to what action to take. Sugriv, Angad, Hanuman and others voiced their opinions. Some viewed Vibhishan's arrival with suspicion and thought he was a spy. Others thought that he was genuine in his intent. Eventually, Ram decided, "It is my duty to accept all who seek my refuge. So, go and bring Vibhishan to me."

The monkeys applauded Ram's generosity and wisdom and brought Vibhishan to him. Vibhishan fell at Ram's feet and again narrated his story. Having accepted Vibhishan on his side, Ram asked him about the strength and set up of Ravan's army. Vibhishan revealed to Ram all he knew of Ravan's methods, strategy and the size of his army.

A Bridge to Lanka

Sensing victory was near, Ram, Lakshman, Sugriv, Hanuman and the thousands of monkey and bear warriors, who had gathered to help in the rescue of Sita, headed south. Soon they reached the ocean and wondered how to cross it, since not everyone could leap across like Hanuman.

Ram appealed to Samudra, the ocean-god for help. Samudra appeared and told Ram, "Nala, one of the monkey warriors on your side, is the son of Vishwakarma – the architect of the gods. He has inherited the wisdom and skill of his father. To reach the opposite shore, allow him to build a bridge. He has the expertise to accomplish this task." Ram agreed to the idea and Nala was assigned this great, important work. Immediately, he gathered the other monkeys and explained to them their duties. As instructed, the monkeys hurriedly collected the materials necessary to build the bridge. With their immense strength, the monkey warriors carried giants rocks to the shore. As they placed each rock, they faithfully chanted the name of Ram to ensure that it would stay afloat. The pace and enthusiasm of their work increased as they reached nearer their destination. Thus, under the guidance of Nala, the sturdy bridge was constructed in five days. Everyone admired the magnificent bridge and prepared to cross over.

Ram led the army onto the bridge and headed towards Lanka. As they crossed, the monkeys danced with joy, occasionally jumping into the sea for a refreshing swim. Soon, the entire army crossed the ocean and arrived on the shores of Lanka ready for the task ahead. Here, they pitched camp at a suitable place.

Angad in Ravan's Palace

With the huge army camped on the shore, Ram decided to give Ravan one final chance for peace by returning Sita. He selected Angad, Vali's son, to go to Ravan as his messenger and convey the offer to him. The brave Angad was prepared and soon reached Ravan's palace. He entered the hall and found Ravan in consultation with his ministers. Angad stood boldly before them and delivered Ram's message.

Angad spoke glowingly of Ram's valour and strength. He warned Ravan that if he did not return Sita then he would be vanquished. All this praise of Ram angered Ravan and so he ridiculed Angad. However, Angad, who had great faith in Ram's powers, stamped his foot on the floor and challenged, "If you can move my leg then Ram will withdraw and you can have Sita."

Immediately, Ravan ordered his men to seize Angad's leg and crush him. Ravan's warriors were delighted to be given this opportunity and rushed to topple Angad. Despite their combined efforts, Angad's leg did not move. Seeing them fail, Ravan came off his throne and tried. As Ravan grasped his foot, Angad taunted him, "You cannot be saved by grasping my foot. Why don't you surrender at Ram's feet." Ravan, too, failed and returned to his throne, despondent.

Angad then left and told Ram of the events in Ravan's court. With Ravan's refusal to release Sita, Ram had no choice but to attack. He ordered the monkeys to move forward into battle. They swiftly captured many prime positions.

Ravan countered by sending Indrajit, his son. He shot serpent arrows and with them felled Ram and Lakshman, making them unconscious. But with the arrival of the serpents' arch enemy, Garud, the eagle, the effect of the serpent arrows vanished, reviving Ram and Lakshman.

One by one, Ravan sent his generals into battle and they were all killed. Out of desperation, he awoke his giant brother, Kumbhakaran, who slept for six months at a time. Kumbhakaran advised Ravan to return Sita, but Ravan angrily refused. Kumbhakaran, out of brotherly love, agreed to fight Ram. But he, too, was soon killed in a fierce battle that shook the earth.

Ravan, desperate and pained by the death of so many relatives and close friends, was fearful of losing the battle.

Hanuman Brings the Healing Herbs

Seeing his disheartened father, Indrajit comforted Ravan and vowed to defeat the enemy. He again entered the battlefield and threw his Brahmastra which hit Ram and Lakshman and knocked them unconscious.

As they lay lifeless, Jambuvan sent Hanuman to fetch the healing herbs from the Aushadhi Parvat – a hill between the Kailas and Rishabh mountains. He told Hanuman that there were four types of healing herbs there which glowed in the dark and illuminated the surroundings. Hanuman immediately made his way there, but could not recognise the healing herbs from the ordinary ones. So he picked up the entire hill and carried it across the ocean to where Ram and Lakshman lay unconscious. With the application of the healing herbs, Ram and Lakshman regained consciousness and their wounds healed. With their revival, the army of monkeys gained new strength.

Indrajit then used his powers to create an illusory form of Sita and while Hanuman and the monkeys looked on helplessly, he killed her. This news was relayed to Ram, who was shocked. But Vibhishan reasoned that Ravan would not have allowed Sita to be killed due to his lust for her and that Indrajit had used this decoy to direct attention away from the *yagna* he wanted to perform. Vibhishan warned Ram, "If the *yagna* is completed by Indrajit he will become very difficult to defeat." So, immediately Ram sent Vibhishan, Lakshman and a select group of monkeys to the place where Indrajit had started the *yagna* to stop him.

They rushed to Nikumbhila and entered the area where Indrajit had already began the *yagna*. Lakshman challenged Indrajit, who was surprised to see them. He was furious that his *yagna* had been interrupted and remained incomplete. Indrajit fired his arrows at Lakshman. A ferocious duel ensued and, eventually, Lakshman attacked Indrajit with the Indraastra and killed him.

When news of Indrajit's demise reached Ravan, he was heartbroken and furious.

The Defeat of Ravan

With his brothers, sons and army generals defeated, Ravan decided to join the battle himself. Angry and eager for revenge, he called for his chariot and set out for the battlefield.

Ram was waiting on the battlefield. He was a tower of strength and with his glorious bow in hand, radiated confidence and sparkled like the sun.

With Ravan's entry, they let fly arrows at each other, without either gaining the upper hand.

Then, Lakshman, who was with Ram, became impatient and shot a volley of arrows at Ravan. Angered by this, Ravan hurled his Shakti weapon at Lakshman which knocked him down like a thunderbolt.

Ram was distressed when he saw Lakshman lying unconscious. Sushena, the army physician, asked Hanuman to once again bring the healing herbs. When the herbs were brought, Lakshman regained consciousness.

This gave Ram renewed strength and he focussed on the task of defeating Ravan. Before long, Ram and Ravan faced each other again in a head-on battle. Both released powerful weapons at the other. Both were renowned for their fighting skills and countered each other, blow for blow. As they chased and evaded one another, the tension on both sides was visible. Then, finally, Ram unleashed the Brahmastra which fatally struck Ravan, thus killing him and bringing the war to an end.

There was joy all around at Ram's victory. It was a victory of good over evil, righteousness over unrighteousness, that is, *dharma* over *adharma*.

Sita Passes the Fire Test

With the battle over and Ravan dead, Ram declared Vibhishan as the new king of Lanka. After performing the funeral rites of Ravan, Vibhishan was coronated. He then rushed to Ram for his blessings.

Ram instructed Hanuman to go to Sita in Ashok Vatika, where she had been held captive, and inform her of Ravan's defeat. Hanuman duly obeyed and returned with a message for Ram that Sita was eager to be reunited with him.

So, Ram requested Vibhishan, "Go to Sita. Let her have a holy bath, dress in royal clothes and ornaments and then bring her to me." Vibhishan made all arrangements for Sita's reunion with Ram and brought her to him in a decorated palanquin. However, Ram's reception was cold. He said to Sita, "As a Kshatriya I have fulfilled my duty and rescued you. But you have lived in a stranger's house for a year and so I cannot take you with me. You are free to go where you wish."

Everyone was stunned by Ram's remarks. But, calmly, Sita replied, "Your words do not befit you. Believe me when I tell you that I am innocent of any wrongdoing. I have remained pure and chaste throughout my imprisonment. I am prepared to prove my innocence by undergoing the fire test."

Lakshman now looked at Ram in anger, but as instructed, prepared the fire as the entire army watched in suspense.

With the fire in full blaze, Sita bowed to Ram and prayed to her mother, Earth, "If I am innocent then may Agni, the god of fire, protect me." She circumambulated the blazing fire and then flung herself in as everyone looked on helplessly. There were gasps of agony amid the stunned silence.

After a few moments, Agni emerged out of the fire, with Sita before him. He declared to Ram, "Sita is returned to you. She is pure and chaste."

There was great relief and joy all round.

Ram had known all along of Sita's purity, but since he was the upholder of Dharma, he allowed this fire ordeal to convince everyone else of her purity.

Return to Ayodhya

The next morning, Ram expressed his wish to return to Ayodhya and meet his brother, Bharat. Vibhishan brought the Pushpak Viman, a special flying chariot, and requested Ram to accept it.

Ram thanked Vibhishan, Sugriv, Hanuman and all others who had helped him to defeat Ravan and rescue Sita. He asked for their permission to leave. Vibhishan, his ministers, Sugriv and all the monkeys and bears also wanted to accompany Ram. He agreed. So, they all climbed aboard the divine flying chariot which had room for them all. Then, along with Sita and Lakshman, Ram sat in the Pushpak Viman and flew away.

As they sped towards Ayodhya, Ram showed Sita the various sites they had searched for her, the route they had taken and recalled the contribution of all those who had helped him to rescue her. He pointed out the scene of the battle, the bridge built by Nala, the Rishyamuk mountain where they had first met Hanuman and Sugriv, their hermitage at Panchvati and many other landmarks.

Ram landed at the ashram of Sage Bharadvaj and sent Hanuman to inform Bharat of his return.

Hanuman disguised himself as a human and went to meet Bharat in Nandigram. Hanuman spotted the simply-clad Bharat and informed him of Ram's arrival. Bharat was elated by the news and asked Hanuman to narrate what had happened to Ram over the years. He described the many adventures of Ram and then told Bharat to prepare for his return to Ayodhya the following day.

Bharat, Shatrughna, Kaushalya and all the people of Ayodhya were overjoyed as they prepared a fitting royal welcome for the triumphant return of their king.

The Coronation of Ram and Sita

The following day, Ram, Sita and Lakshman, accompanied by Vibhishan, Sugriv, Hanuman and all the monkeys and bears, entered Ayodhya to a joyous welcome.

Ram bowed with respect to all. Amid the celebratory atmosphere, everyone watched with bated breath as Ram fell at the feet of Kaikeyi, who had been the cause of all the turmoil. There was not a single sign of anger on Ram's face as he bowed to Kaikeyi. In fact, with a huge smile, he thanked her for the opportunity she had presented him. Elaborating, he said, "By leaving Ayodhya and going to the forest I learnt of my father's love and attachment for me; of Bharat's brotherly love, since he renounced the throne that he was entitled to; of Hanumanji's strength while searching for Sita; of Sugriv's true friendship; of Lakshman's devotion, since he left behind his wife to stay with me in the forest; of Sita's purity and fidelity, since she passed the fire test; of my own strength in my fight with Ravan; and of what enemies are like through Ravan's enmity towards me. All this I have learnt by your blessings."

After this emotional reunion, Bharat greeted Ram and returned his sandals as he requested Ram to take his rightful seat on the throne as the king of Koshal.

Ram accepted Bharat's wish. The necessary arrangements were made while Ram and Sita had the ritual bath. Sage Vasishtha, the royal guru, then performed the coronation ceremony.

Ram praised the efforts of all who had helped him to defeat Ravan, rescue Sita and return safely to Ayodhya.

Even the gods sent gifts to the newly crowned king and queen. Ram, in turn, distributed gifts to the Brahmins and all his allies. Sita gave a pearl necklace to Hanuman.

Thereafter, Ram ruled his kingdom with integrity and justice. There was peace, prosperity and happiness throughout his kingdom. The period of his reign became known as Ram Rajya, which has been looked upon as an ideal for creating a perfect nation.

Ram Renounces Sita

Ram often sent his advisers to find out the views and needs of his subjects. Once Durmukh, one of his most trusted ministers, returned with the message that all were very happy. However, he reported, "Some criticise you for keeping Sita even after she had stayed with Ravan for such a long time. They say the path you have taken will set a bad example to the people."

Hearing this report Ram was disturbed. He went for a walk and heard a washerman voice the same criticism. He returned to his palace with a heavy heart.

He knew that Sita was pure, chaste and faithful, yet to rule the kingdom with justice he took the tough decision to part with Sita. He called Lakshman and told him of his decision. He instructed, "Take Sita across the Ganga and tell her only after you have crossed over."

Lakshman thus carried out this difficult and emotionally painful task. He cried openly as he broke the news of Ram's decision to Sita. She, too, wept and requested Lakshman to inform Ram, "I am not displeased with him. Tell him not to banish me from his heart. I will forever be his disciple and subject. He is god and the king of Ayodhya."

Sita's words echoed the sublime understanding of an ideal wife.

With this, Lakshman left Sita, who was pregnant, in the care of Sage Valmiki and returned to Ayodhya.

Lav and Kush

Sage Valmiki placed Sita under the care of the women in his ashram. Sometime later Sita gave birth to twin boys. Valmiki named them Lav and Kush – based on the names of the bottom and top part of the *darbh* grass.

These two princes were virtuous, brave and skillful. Valmiki taught them the Ramayan, which they sang in their melodious voices.

Once, Ram was performing an Ashwamedh Yagna. The sacrificial horse was let loose to wander the country and receive the reverence of all the subjects. However, when the horse passed through Valmiki's ashram, Lav and Kush tied it to a tree.

Shatrughna, who had been following the horse, saw all this and requested them to release it. The boys refused and challenged him, "Fight with us and you can take the horse if you defeat us." Shatrughna was unable to defeat them and so summoned help. Ram also came to retrieve the horse. It was then that Ram learnt that Lav and Kush were his sons. He was overjoyed. The boys bowed respectfully to Ram and returned the horse.

Ram had invited Sita to participate in the *yagna*. Sitaji was delighted and thought to herself, "Ram had renounced me only for the sake of his *dharma*, but in his heart he has complete love for me only. Otherwise he would have remarried, but he hasn't. Instead he has made a golden replica of me and carried out his duties."

The next morning, Sita arrived with Sage Valmiki to the *yagna* arena. The wise sage announced, "Sita will take a pledge to prove her innocence of any wrongdoing and establish her purity." Ram then said, "I know that Sita is pure and innocent, but I had to renounce her to avoid public criticism. Please forgive me."

Then Sita declared her pledge, "O Mother Earth! If I am pure and innocent of any wrongdoing, may I enter back into the earth from where I came." Instantly the ground opened up and with her focus on Ram, Sita returned to Mother Earth.

Bhagwan Swaminarayan and the Ramayan

Bhagwan Swaminarayan, called Ghanshyam in His childhood, was born in Chhapaiya, near Ayodhya. His father was Dharmadev and his mother, Bhaktimata. When Ghanshyam was three-years-old, Dharmadev moved his family to Ayodhya. There, Ghanshyam visited the Hanuman Gadhi and other mandirs daily and listened to narrations of the Ramayan with great interest. He also studied the scriptures under the tutelage of Dharmadev, who was a very proficient and respected scholar. At the age of eleven, Ghanshyam left home and embarked on a seven-year pilgrimage of India. During this time, He was known as Nilkanth Varni and He continually recited the numerous scriptural passages He had memorised. Among them were many couplets and verses from the Ramayan. Thus, from a young age, Bhagwan Swaminarayan developed a deep insight into the Ramayan.

The Ramayan is a rich and powerful story which provides many inspiring messages. The lives of the characters and the plot have been analysed and praised by scholars, devotees and laymen for thousands of years to reveal these inspiring messages.

In the Swaminarayan Sampraday, the Ramayan is held in high esteem since it is a pillar of Hindu culture and tradition. It teaches unity, love, brotherhood, family values, duty and many other inspiring messages which are relevant even today in helping individuals, families and societies to live together peacefully and happily.

The Ramayan teaches that God and His holy Sadhu are the torchbearers of

Sanatan Hindu Dharma. Today, this ideal is upheld by His Divine Holiness Pramukh Swami Maharaj, in the tradition founded by Bhagwan Swaminarayan.

In the Vachanamrut – a compilation of the divine spiritual discourses of Bhagwan Swaminarayan – He has used examples from the Ramayan to convey various spiritual messages.

The following is a collection of some of these references, though the particular stories referred to may not have been included in this publication.

TRUE DEVOTEES HAVE TRUE LOVE FOR GOD

In Vachanamrut Gadhada I-59, Bhagwan Swaminarayan says, "A devotee does indeed have unparalleled love for God; he is simply not aware of it. Only when someone points it out to the devotee does he realise." He gives the example of Hanumanji to illustrate this, "Hanumanji possessed immense strength, but he did not realise it until someone else revealed it to him."

Here, Bhagwan Swaminarayan refers to the time when, in the search for Sita, someone was needed to cross the vast ocean to reach Lanka. At that time, Jambuvan reminded Hanuman that he, Hanuman, was the son of the god of wind and was capable of jumping across the ocean and completing that task. Hanuman subsequently rose to the challenge and successfully completed the mission. Similarly, true devotees, because of their humility, often do not realise the extent of their own devotion.

UNDERSTAND GOD AS DIVINE

God in the human form may not be recognised since He performs actions just like any other ordinary human. Despite these apparently human traits, God is divine in all situations. This is the understanding of a true devotee of God; one who has fully understood His glory.

In Vachanamrut Gadhada II-10, Bhagwan Swaminarayan emphasises this need to view all actions of God as divine, "In the *avatar* of Ram, He (God) broke the bow and also dispelled the strife of the deities by killing wicked persons such as Ravan. These and other such exploits are known as the divine actions of God.

"However, when Sita was abducted, Raghunathji [Ram] appeared to have become insane and was constantly crying....These and other such actions of God appear to be human-like." But, to a true devotee, they are indeed divine.

Understanding like That of Sita

In Vachanamrut Gadhada III-11, Bhagwan Swaminarayan explains that a devotee who is truly attached to God will not forsake worship of God, even under the most testing and adverse circumstances. Then, to illustrate this, He describes how Sita did not waver from her devotion despite being exiled, without fault, to the forest.

He says, "When Jankiji [Sitaji] was exiled to the forest by Ramchandraji, she began to lament. Lakshmanji was very sorrowful at that time as well. But then Sitaji explained to Lakshmanji, 'I am not crying because of my own grief; I am crying for the grief of Ramchandraji. Because Raghunathji is extremely compassionate, and since he has exiled me to the forest out of fear of public accusation, he must be thinking, 'I have sent Sita to the forest without any fault of her own.' Knowing this and being compassionate, he must be experiencing severe grief in his mind. So please tell Ramchandraji, 'Sita is not distressed; she will go to Valmiki Rishi's hermitage and happily engage in your worship there. So do not feel any remorse on account of Sita's distress.' Sitaji sent this message with Lakshmanji, but in no way did she perceive faults in Ramchandraji."

True Knowledge Frees from Worldly Desires

Throughout the Vachanamrut Bhagwan Swaminarayan has stressed the need to develop *gnan* – true knowledge of the nature of God and *atma* – since, only then is it possible to become free of all worldly desires and attachments and offer true devotion to God.

In Vachanamrut Gadhada III-39, Bhagwan Swaminarayan describes how *gnan* is effective in freeing one of all material desires, "When Hanumanji brought the Vishalyakarani herbal medicine for Ramchandra and gave it to him to drink, all of the arrows from Ramchandraji's body fell out by themselves. Similarly, all of the 'arrows' in the form of the *indriyas'* desires to indulge in the *vishays* are removed when these two points have been imbedded in a person's mind." So, when knowledge of the two – God and *atma* – is attained, one is freed from all desires for and attachment to worldly pleasures.

'Yati' – A True Celibate

In Vachanamrut Jetalpur-2, Bhagwan Swaminarayan uses the examples of Hanuman and Lakshman to describe the characteristics of a *yati* – one who observes *brahmacharya* and has control over all his senses.

Bhagwan Swaminarayan says, "When, on Ramchandraji's instruction, Hanumanji went to Lanka in search of Sitaji, in order to recognise Sitaji he looked at the faces of all of the women in Lanka. As he continued looking, he thought, 'This is not Jankiji... This one is not Jankiji...' Then, while he was thinking this, he saw Mandodari and thought, 'Could this be Jankiji?' But then he concluded in his mind that because of her separation from Ramchandraji, Jankiji's body would never be so healthy, and she would never be able to sleep so soundly. With this thought in mind, Hanumanji turned back. Then he doubted in his mind, 'I am a 'yati', but could a flaw have developed in me by seeing all these women?' But then he reconciled to himself, 'How can there be any flaw in me? It is because of Ramchandraji's instruction to find Sitaji that I had to look at all of these women.' He also thought, 'By Ramchandraji's grace, no disturbance has arisen in my *indriyas* and in my *vrutti*.' Thinking this, he wandered unreservedly to look for Sitaji. In this way, like Hanumanji, one whose *antahkaran* remains pure despite being faced by such vicious influences is called a 'yati'.

"Moreover, while searching for Sitaji in the forest after she was abducted, Ramchandraji and Lakshmanji came to the place where Sugriv was seated on the Fatak Shila. There, they informed Sugriv, 'We have come here because Jankiji has been abducted. So if you know of her whereabouts, please tell us.' Sugriv replied, 'Maharaj, I did hear the cries, 'O Ram! O Ram!' coming from the sky. Also, some pieces of jewellery, which are tied in this piece of cloth, were dropped from above. I have kept them with me.' Thereupon Raghunathji requested, 'Please bring them here so that we can check them.' Sugriv thus brought the jewellery to Raghunathji. Raghunathji took the pieces of jewellery and showed them to Lakshmanji. First he showed ornaments worn on the ears, then he showed bracelets and other ornaments worn on the arms, but Lakshmanji did not recognise any of these. He was then shown some anklets. Lakshmanji immediately exclaimed, 'Maharaj! These are Jankiji's anklets!' Hearing this, Raghunathji inquired, 'Lakshmanji, how is it that you did not recognise the other ornaments and recognised these anklets?' Lakshmanji replied, 'Maharaj, I have never seen Jankiji's body. In fact, except for her feet, I have not seen any other part of Sitaji's body. The only reason I have been able to recognise the anklets is because whenever I used to go and bow at her feet every evening, I would see her anklets.' In this way, despite the fact that for 14 years Lakshmanji was in their service, with the exception of Jankiji's feet, he had never intentionally seen her body. Such a person should be known as a 'yati'."

Glossary

adharma	unrighteousness
Agastya	sage insulted by Tataka
Agni	the fire-god
Akampa	a demon who escaped from Janasthan to report to Ravan
Aksha	a son of Ravan
Angad	son of Vali
Ansuya	wife of Sage Atri
antahkaran	mind
Ashok Vatika	beautiful garden where Ravan imprisoned Sita
Ashvapati	king of the Kekeya kingdom; father of Queen Kaikeyi
Ashwamedh Yagna	special sacrifice in which a horse is released to traverse the kingdom and return uncaptured
Atharva Veda	the fourth Veda
Atibala	one of the powerful mantras taught by Vishwamitra to Ram
atma	soul
Atri	sage whom Ram met during his exile
Aushadhi Parvat	the hill on which the healing herbs grew
avatar	incarnation of God
Atri	sage in whose ashram Ram, Sita and Lakshman stayed for some time during their exile
Bala	one of the powerful mantras taught by Vishwamitra to Ram

Bhaktimata	mother of Bhagwan Swaminarayan
Bharadvaj	sage whom Ram visited first on leaving Ayodhya
Bharat	second son of King Dashrath, born of Kaikeyi
brahmacharya	celibacy
Brahmastra	weapon presided over by Brahma
Daksh	father-in-law of Shiv
darbh	a type of grass
darshan	to see with reverence and devotion
Dashrath	king of the Koshal kingdom; father of Ram
Devraat	ancestor of King Janak who was given the mighty bow by Shiv
Dhanu	a heavenly being cursed to live as the demon Kabandh
dharma	righteousness
Dharmadev	father of Bhagwan Swaminarayan
Durmukh	minister of Ram who reported the public opinion to him
Dushana	brother of Khara
Garud	the eagle
Ghanshyam	childhood name of Bhagwan Swaminarayan
gnan	knowledge
Guha	a hunter-king in whose hermitage Ram, Sita and Lakshman stayed for a while
Hanuman	son of the wind-god and minister of Sugriv
Hanuman Gadhi	the mandir of Hanuman where Ghanshyam went daily for *darshan*
Ikshvaku	the dynasty into which Ram was born
Indraastra	a weapon presided over by Indra

Indrajit	a son of Ravan
indriya	a sense by which one perceives
Janak	king of the Videha kingdom; father of Sita
Janki	another name for Sita
Jatayu	the eagle king and friend of King Dashrath
Kabandh	a demon who was formerly Dhanu
Kaikeyi	mother of Bharat
Kand	section
Kaushalya	mother of Ram
Khara	a half-brother of Ravan
kraunch	a type of bird
Kshatriya	one of the four social classes of Indian society; the ruler and warrior class
Kumbhakaran	the giant brother of Ravan
Kush	one of the twin sons of Ram and brother of Lav
Kushadhvaj	brother of King Janak
Lakshman	son of King Dashrath; one of the twins born to Sumitra
Lakshman Rekha	line drawn on the ground by Lakshman around the hermitage to protect Sita
Lav	one of the twin sons of Ram and brother of Kush
Lord Brahma	inspired Valmiki to compose the Ramayan
Mandvi	daughter of Kushadhvaj; wife of Bharat
Manthara	the hunch-back maid who poisoned Kaikeyi's mind
Marich	uncle of Ravan, who lured Ram away from the hermitage by assuming the form of a golden deer

Maryada Purushottam	description of Ram as the ideal upholder of *dharma*
Matang Rishi	guru of Shabri
Nala	architect of the monkeys who built the stone bridge across the ocean to Lanka; son of Vishwakarma
Naradji	revealed the glory and story of Ram to Valmiki
Nilkanth Varni	name by which Bhagwan Swaminarayan was known during His pilgrimage of India
Parshuram	son of Sage Jamadagni who challenged Ram to string the bow of Vishnu
payasam	sweetened milk and rice mixture
Pushpak Viman	flying chariot provided by Vibhishan for Ram to return to Ayodhya
Putrakam Yagna	special sacrifice performed with the desire to get a son
Raghunath	another name for Ram
Ram	the central character of the Ramayan; eldest son of King Dashrath, born of Kaushalya
Ram Rajya	the period of Ram's rule; recognised as the perfect style of government
Ravan	King of Lanka who kidnapped Sita
Rishyashringa	son of Sage Vibhandak who performed the Putrakam Yagna for King Dashrath
Samudra	the ocean-god
Sanatan Hindu Dharma	the original name of the Hindu religion
Shabri	devout old lady devotee who served the rishis
Shatrughna	son of King Dashrath and one of the twins born to Sumitra
Shiv	son-in-law of Daksh who gave his mighty bow to Devraat
shlok	verses in Sanskrit
Shrutakirti	daughter of Kushadhvaj; wife of Shatrughna
Sita	also called Janki. Daughter of King Janak; wife of Ram

Subahu	demon killed by Ram for trying to sabotage Vishwamitra's *yagna*
Sugriv	younger brother of Vali, who helped Ram to recapture Sita with his army of monkeys
Sumantra	King Dashrath's senior minister
Sumitra	mother of the twins, Lakshman and Shatrughna
Sunayana	mother of Sita
Sund	husband of Tataka
Surpankha	sister of Ravan who desired to marry Ram
Tataka	mother of Marich
Urmila	daughter of King Janak; wife of Lakshman
Vachanamrut	spiritual discourses of Bhagwan Swaminarayan
Vali	King of Kishkindha, brother of Sugriv
Valmiki	author of the Ramayan
Vasishtha	guru of King Dashrath
Vibhishan	younger brother of Ravan who joined with Ram
Vishalyakarni	one of the special healing herbs
vishays	worldly pleasures
Vishnu	deity who presented a mighty bow to Parshuram
Vishwakarma	architect of the gods who made the two bows given to Shiv and Vishnu
Vishwamitra	renowned sage who took Ram's help to complete his *yagna*
vrutti	focus; attention
yagna	a ritual sacrifice performed with the purpose of achieving a particular desire
Yaksha	a divine being
yati	a celibate